MW00604897

Amazing Words

Old Testament

New Testament

HOW GREAT YOU ARE, SOVEREIGN LORD! THERE IS NO ONE LIKE YOU, AND THERE IS NO GOD BUT YOU, AS WE HAVE HEARD WITH OUR OWN EARS.

2 Samuel 7:22

PENTA TEUCH

book of GENESIS

CREATION
AND
THE FALL
(Genesis 1-3)

In the beginning, God created the heavens and the earth. (Genesis 1:1)

These are the opening words of the Bible. God created the world in seven days. On the first day, He separated the light from the darkness. On the second day, he separated the water in the sky and on land and created the atmosphere. On the third day, He bunched the water together and separated it from land. On the fourth day, He created the sun, moon, and stars. On the fifth day, He created birds and sea creatures. On the sixth day, God created land animals and Adam and Eve, the first human beings, and placed them in a garden called Eden. Humanity was the crowning achievement of God's creation as they were created in God's image. Finally, God rested on the seventh day as a commemoration of the work He had done and pronounced His creation good.

God placed two trees in the garden: the Tree of Life and the Tree of the Knowledge of Good and Evil. One tree provided fruit that led to life, and the other was a test of obedience from God. God instructed the new couple not to go near or touch the tree, or they would die. For some reason, Adam and Eve found themselves near the tree, and a serpent spoke to Eve to tempt her to eat the fruit. The serpent promised Eve that if she ate, her eyes would be open, and she would be like God, knowing good from evil. Eve took the fruit and gave it to Adam, and they both ate. Because of this act of disobedience, a curse was pronounced on all of their descendants. The ground was cursed in that it would be difficult to produce food, and the woman's womb was cursed to cause pain during childbirth. Finally, Adam and Eve were cast out of the Garden so they would no longer have access to the Tree of Life.

book of GENESIS

CAIN AND ABEL

(Genesis 4)

Adam and Eve had two sons, Cain and Abel. Cain grew up to be a farmer and Abel a shepherd. One day, the two sons went to offer sacrifice to the Lord. Cain offered some of the fruits of his harvest, while Abel brought a lamb. Abel's offering pleased the Lord while Cain's did not. This made Cain very jealous and angry, and he killed his brother Abel. This angered the Lord, and God confronted Cain. Because of this evil deed, Cain was marked by God and cast out to wander the earth. Eventually, Cain settled in the land of Nod. It was Cain's son and descendants that built the first cities.

The story goes on that God blessed Adam and Eve with another son, Seth. It was Seth's descendants that maintained the worship of the True God.

book of GENESIS

NOAH'S ARK

(Genesis 6-9)

Over time, humanity became increasingly wicked and forgot about God. It got so bad that every thought they had was continuously evil. God regretted that He had made humanity and decided that they needed to be destroyed. However, there was one man, Noah, who was righteous and who served God faithfully. God appeared to Noah and commanded him to build an ark to save his family, animals, and as many people as would listen to his message because He would destroy the world with a flood. It took Noah 120 years to complete the ark. During that 120 years, he also preached to those around him about the coming doom. Unfortunately, no one listened to Noah's warnings, and only his immediate family was saved.

Once Noah and his family entered the ark, it rained for 40 days and 40 nights, flooding the earth, in addition to underground fountains and water coming up. After the rain subsided, the ark continued to float for around another year. After about 150 days, God caused a wind to come to help the waters subside, and the ark came to rest in a mountain range called Ararat. Noah released a raven and a dove out to see if they could locate some land. They both returned. Finally, after another week, Noah sent out another dove, and the dove did not return. Then Noah and his family knew it was safe to leave the ark.

Once they disembarked, God spoke to Noah and made a covenant that he would never again destroy the world by water and put a rainbow in the sky as a sign of that covenant. God then commanded Noah and his family to repopulate the earth.

book of GENESIS

ABRAHAM
AND
ISAAC
(Genesis 12-22)

A couple of centuries after Noah, God again revealed himself to a man named Abram. Abram lived in a place called Ur, which was somewhere in the area of Babylon. God spoke to Abram and instructed him to leave his home and go to the land of Canaan. God would bless him and multiply his descendants and would give them this land so that they would be a light for him. The problem was that Abram and his wife Sara did not have any children and apparently couldn't have children! Nonetheless, God promised that he would bless them with children and would multiply their descendants.

Sometime later, God appeared to Abram again and made a covenant with him. The sign of this covenant was the ritual of circumcision. God also changed Abram and Sarai's names to Abraham and Sarah and again promised them many descendants. However, Sarah and Abraham doubted God's promise, and Sarah proposed that Abraham take her servant Hagar to bear children on her behalf. Abraham listened and had a son named Ishmael through Hagar.

However, God did keep his promise to Abraham, and Sarah and Sarah bore a son named Isaac. Sometime later, God again appeared to Abraham and instructed him to take Isaac on a mountain and offer him as a sacrifice to the Lord. Abraham hesitantly prepared to obey. Upon reaching the site of the sacrifice, Isaac inquired what they were going to sacrifice as they didn't bring along any animals. Abraham revealed to Isaac that he was to be the sacrifice. Isaac submitted to the will of the Lord. But just when Abraham was ready to do the deed, an angel stopped him! God told him not to lay a hand on the child and instead provided a ram for the sacrifice.

book of
GENESIS

JACOB
AND
ESAU
(Genesis 25-27)

Abraham's son Isaac married a woman named Rebekkah, and they had twin boys named Jacob and Esau. Even though they were twins, Esau was considered the oldest because he was born first. Esau was also very hairy and red. As they grew up, Esau was a hunter and was favored by his father, Isaac, and Jacob was a shepherd and was favored by his mother, Rebekkah.

As the firstborn, Esau would be the main recipient of Isaac's inheritance. One day, Esau came back from a hunt and was very hungry. Jacob was making a pot of stew, and Esau asked for some. Jacob saw this as an opportunity. He offered Esau some stew if he agreed to trade his birthright or inheritance. Esau agreed.

Sometime later, Isaac was on his deathbed. Knowing this, he called for Esau so that he could give him the blessing of the firstborn. He asked him first to go and hunt for a deer and to prepare it the way he liked. While Esau was on the hunt, Jacob and Rebekkah concocted a plan to have Jacob receive the blessing. She instructed Jacob to go and take two goats and tie their skin to his arms and neck while she would prepare the meat in the way Isaac liked. Then Jacob would take the meal to Isaac and receive the blessing of the firstborn, which would designate Jacob as the head of the family because Isaac was now blind.

Finally, Jacob went into Isaac's tent. Isaac was suspicious because while Jacob's arms and neck felt like Esau's, his voice still sounded like Jacob's. However, upon Jacob's word that he was, in fact, Esau, Isaac pronounced the blessing on him. When Esau returned from his hunt, he entered Isaac's tent to receive the blessing. When Esau learned that Jacob had stolen his blessing, he was enraged and threatened to kill Jacob. As a result, Jacob fled to the land of Haran to live with his uncle Laban.

book of GENESIS

JOSEPH AND HIS BROTHERS

(Genesis 37-50)

Jacob had twelve sons. His two youngest sons, Joseph and Benjamin, were born from his favorite wife, Rachel, and, therefore, were his favorite sons. Because of Jacob's favoritism, his other sons became jealous of Joseph. One day, Jacob made Joseph a colorful coat that designated Joseph, the second youngest, as the next head of the family, bypassing the ten older sons. This enraged his brothers. God had also given Joseph the gift of dreams. One night, Joseph dreamt that he and his eleven brothers were tying bundles of wheat and that the bundles stood up and all bowed down to his. He also dreamt that the sun, moon, and stars all bowed down to him. He told these dreams to his brothers, which caused them to hate him even more. They began to plot for a way to get rid of him.

Sometime later, the brothers were out finding pastures for the sheep. Jacob sent Joseph to check on them. As the brothers saw him approaching, they conspired to kill him. However, the oldest brother, Reuben, suggested instead that they throw him into a nearby empty well. They grabbed him, stripped him of his coat, and threw him in. Shortly after, they saw a caravan of Ishmaelites passing by, and they sold him into slavery in Egypt. Once in Egypt, Joseph was sold to a man named Potiphar, who was the captain of Pharaoh's court. God showed favor on Joseph, and he was soon placed in charge of Potiphar's entire household. However, Potiphar's wife tried to seduce Joseph, and when he resisted, he was thrown into prison. God again had favor on Joseph, and he rose to be in charge of the prison.

Sometime after, the Pharaoh's baker and cupbearer were thrown into the prison. They were both troubled with dreams, so Joseph went to interpret them. Joseph explained that the dreams were saying that the baker would be executed and the cupbearer would be released and returned to Pharaoh's court.

It happened just as he had said. Years later, Pharaoh himself was troubled with strange dreams. The cupbearer remembered Joseph and told Pharaoh. Pharaoh summoned Joseph from the prison, and Joseph successfully interpreted his dream. As a result, Joseph was placed as second in command in all of Egypt. Years later, a famine swept across the land, but because of Joseph's foresight and leadership, Egypt still had plenty of food. People from surrounding countries came to Egypt for grain. One day, Joseph's brothers appeared seeking food. Joseph recognized them, but they did not recognize him. Joseph proceeded to test them to see if they had changed. He kept one of them as a prisoner and then sent the others home with the grain they needed on the condition that they return with his baby brother, Benjamin. When they returned, Joseph then instructed his servant to place his chalice in Benjamin's bag of grain. He then sent soldiers after them to retrieve it. Joseph threatened to keep Benjamin in Egypt as punishment. The brothers refused, knowing that losing Benjamin would kill their father. They offered to stay in his place. That is when Joseph knew that they had changed and revealed his true identity to them. He brought them and his father to stay with him in Egypt.

book of EXODUS

MOSES
AND THE
BURNING BUSH

(Exodus 1-3)

Many years after Joseph died, a new Pharaoh forgot about him and enslaved the children of Israel. Concerned about their population, and the new Pharaoh decreed the death of all newborn Israelite boys. A woman named Jochebed placed her newborn son in a basket and sent him down the river to save his life. That boy was found by Pharaoh's daughter, who saved him and raised him as her son. She named him Moses.

One day, Moses came across an Egyptian taskmaster beating an Israelite slave. Moses defended the slave and killed the Egyptian. He then fled through the desert to Midian to escape the wrath of Pharaoh. In Midian, he found a wife and became a shepherd.

Years later, while tending the sheep, Moses saw a bush that was on fire but was not burning. When he went to check it out, God spoke to him. God commanded him to go to Pharaoh and tell him to let God's people go. God gave him signs and wonders to show Pharaoh and the children of Israel to prove that he had been sent by God. Moses reluctantly accepted his mission and made his way back to Egypt.

book of EXODUS

PLAGUES OF EGYPT
(Exodus 7-11)

In order to fulfill God's command, Moses had to release a series of signs or plagues on Egypt to convince Pharaoh to let the people go. Some of the signs/plagues that God did through Moses were a staff transforming into a snake, turning the Nile river into blood, plagues of frogs, gnats, flies, death of livestock, locusts, boils, hail, and darkness. All of these plagues were direct affronts to the various gods of Egypt, proving the God of Israel's superiority over them. Still, despite all these plagues, Pharaoh would not let the people go.

PASSOVER
(Exodus 12-13)

Because of Pharaoh's stubbornness, the final and worst plague was pronounced. All the firstborn children in Egypt would die. However, God made provisions to protect the firstborn of Israel. Every household would have to take a lamb and spread its blood on their doorpost. Then they would take the meat to eat with bitter herbs. When the Angel of Death passed by the houses with the blood, it would pass over them. This was the first Passover. The Angel of Death did indeed visit Egypt, and all of the firstborn children died, except for the children of the Israelites. Because of this final plague, Pharaoh finally agreed to let the Israelites go free.

CROSSING THE RED SEA
(Exodus 14)

Once the Pharaoh let the Israelites go, they made their way to the Red Sea in order to pass into Canaan. Pharaoh, however, changed his mind and decided to go after them and bring them back into slavery. So Israel was trapped between Pharaoh's army and the Red Sea. The people began to panic and started to turn on Moses for bringing them out to die. Moses sought the Lord, and God instructed him to lift his staff and to tell the people to go forward. Moses lifted his staff, and God caused a wind to blow throughout the night that split the sea, allowing the Israelites to cross on dry land. As Israel crossed, Pharaoh's army followed them in. Once all of Israel crossed, God caused the wind to cease, and the sea collapsed down on Pharaoh's army, destroying them in the process. Safely on the other side, Israel rejoiced and sang praises to God for his great deliverance.

book of EXODUS

BREAD AND WATER IN THE DESERT

(Exodus 16-17)

Free at last! But freedom comes at a cost. Israel successfully escaped from bondage in Egypt but then found themselves in the desert without enough food or water. The people began to grumble against Moses and even started entertaining the prospect of returning to Egypt! God heard Israel's cries and told Moses to tell the people that quail would be provided for them in the evening for meat, and other food would be provided in the morning.

The next morning, as the Israelites exited their tents, they discovered a light frost-like substance. Moses told them to gather it as this was the bread that the Lord had provided. It was bread from heaven, and they named it manna. The people could gather the manna six days a week, but on the Sabbath, on the seventh day, no manna would be provided, so they had to gather double on the sixth day.

A short time later, the people began to grumble again about water. Again, they turned on Moses to the point where Moses feared for his life. God spoke to Moses and instructed him to go to a large rock and strike the rock with his staff. Moses did as he was told, and when he struck the rock, water flowed out, and the people had enough to drink.

THE GOLDEN CALF

(Exodus 32)

Upon reaching Mt. Sinai (the mountain of God), the children of Israel camped at the base of the mountain, and God commanded Moses to come up the mountain. Moses goes up the mountain, and God gives him the law (Torah) that will govern the religious and civil lives of Israel, including the Ten Commandments. He was on the mountain for 40 days. During those 40 days, the Israelites thought Moses must have died on the mountain. So they pressured Aaron, Moses' brother, to build an idol for them to worship that would represent the God of Israel. Aaron gave in, and the people built a golden calf, and they partied and worshipped it. Moses heard the noise from the mountain, and God told him what was happening. Moses got very angry at what the people had done and smashed the tablets of stone on which God had written the Ten Commandments.

Because of this great sin, God enacted a great punishment on the people, and many of them died. However, God offered mercy for anyone that was willing to repent and come back to God. Those that repented and came back were spared. God always gives us an opportunity before executing judgment!

book of NUMBERS

SPIES GO INTO CANAAN
(Numbers 13)

The Israelites have reached the promised land! They finally made it to the border of Canaan—the land that God promised to Abraham and his descendants. Moses sent spies into the land to scout it out and bring back a report. When the scouts came back, they reported a wonderful land flowing with milk and honey, meaning it was a rich land! However, there was one problem—some of the people that lived in the land were giants, and they had fortified cities with high walls. This report produced a great deal of fear with the people. They began to weep and complain that they had come all of this way to die, and some even proposed killing Moses and returning to Egypt!

However, two of the spies, Joshua and Caleb, told the people that they could take the land! Nonetheless, the people decided to take the counsel of the other spies and turn back to Egypt! Because of this lack of faith, God threatens to wipe them out and make Moses' descendants into a great nation. Moses pleads and intercedes on behalf of the people, and God relents. However, God decreed that no one except Joshua or Caleb would live to enter the promised land. The children of Israel would wander in the wilderness for 40 years, and their children would be the ones to enter.

SERPENTS IN THE WILDERNESS
(Numbers 21)

The Israelites are complaining once again. They are tired of wandering in the wilderness and are again complaining about food and water. Because of their complaining, God removes his protection from them, and poisonous snakes invade the camp. Many people begin to die. Moses intercedes on behalf of the people and asks God to relent his punishment. God instructs Moses to build a bronze serpent and place it on a pole, and anyone that looks at the serpent will be saved. Moses did as he was told, and anyone that was bitten that looked at the serpent was healed.

book of NUMBERS

BALAAM

(Numbers 22-25)

The Israelites were crossing into the territory of Moab. The king of the Moabites, Balak, heard about the Israelites' exploits in other nations and how their God laid waste to Egypt, and they were victorious against any nation that came against them. Because of this, he sought out a sorcerer or magician that could pronounce a curse on the children of Israel. There was such a man named Balaam and Balak sent a delegation to him. Upon being approached by Balak's men, Balaam replied that he had to consult Israel's God before agreeing to anything. That night, God spoke to Balaam and forbade him from saying anything against Israel because they are blessed. Balaam replied to Balak's men that he couldn't do it.

Balak sent more men with more money to convince Balaam to come. He again replied that he couldn't go unless God permitted him and that he would ask again. This time, God told him to go but only to say what He tells him. So Balaam went with the men, but the Bible says that God was angry with him. On the way, God sent an angel to slay Balaam, but Balaam's donkey saw the angel on the road ahead and turned to go a different way. This caused Balaam to hit the animal. This happened a second time, and Balaam beat the donkey again. A third time, the donkey saw the angel again and laid down, which enraged Balaam. Finally, God opened the donkey's mouth, and the donkey asked Balaam why he was beating him and told him he was only looking out for him. God then opened Balaam's eyes so that he could see the angel. The angel told him that if the donkey hadn't stopped, he would have struck Balaam down. Balaam confessed his sin and offered to turn back. The angel told him to go but only to say what God tells him.

Upon arriving at Balak's camp, Balak took Balaam up to a mountain peak where they could see Israel passing by. Three times Balaam opened his mouth to curse Israel, and three times blessings came out! Finally, since Balaam was unable to curse Israel, he told Balak that they could get them to curse themselves. He instructed Balak to send beautiful women into Israel's camp to lead them into sin and idol worship. This caused God to send judgment on the people.

However, two of the spies, Joshua and Caleb, told the people that they could take the land! Nonetheless, the people decided to take the counsel of the other spies and turn back to Egypt! Because of this lack of faith, God threatens to wipe them out and make Moses' descendants into a great nation. Moses pleads and intercedes on behalf of the people, and God relents. However, God decreed that no one except Joshua or Caleb would live to enter the promised land. The children of Israel would wander in the wilderness for 40 years, and their children would be the ones to enter.

book of DEUTERONOMY

DEATH OF MOSES

(Deuteronomy 34)

Towards the end of Israel's wanderings, the people were again complaining against Moses and asking for water. Moses went to God, and God told him to speak to a rock, and the rock would produce water for the people. Moses, however, became very frustrated with the people and struck the rock instead of speaking to it. Because of this, God told him he would not enter the promised land with the people. At 120 years old, Moses gave his final sermon to the camp, appointed Joshua as the next leader of Israel. Then Moses went up on Mt. Nebo and died. The people mourned him for 30 days.

DO YOU NOT
KNOW?
HAVE YOU NOT
HEARD?
THE **LORD** IS
THE **EVERLASTING GOD,**
THE **CREATOR** OF
THE ENDS OF THE EARTH.

HE WILL NOT GROW TIRED OR WEARY,
AND HIS UNDERSTANDING
NO ONE CAN FATHOM.
HE GIVES STRENGTH TO THE WEARY
AND INCREASES THE POWER OF THE WEAK.
EVEN YOUTHS GROW TIRED AND WEARY,
AND YOUNG MEN STUMBLE AND FALL;

BUT **THOSE** WHO HOPE
IN THE **LORD**
WILL RENEW THEIR STRENGTH.
THEY WILL SOAR ON WINGS LIKE EAGLES;
THEY WILL RUN AND NOT GROW WEARY,
THEY WILL WALK AND NOT BE FAINT.

Isaiah 40: 28-31

BOOKS OF HISTORY

book of JOSHUA

RAHAB

(Joshua 2)

After 40 years of aimless wandering in the wilderness, Israel has arrived at the promised land! Moses has died, Joshua is now the leader. They have crossed the river Jordan into Canaan. Now they have come across the first major city in the land, Jericho. Jericho is a heavily fortified city with massively high and thick walls to deter invasion. However, God has appeared to Joshua and assured him that He will be with him. So Joshua selects two men to go into Jericho as spies to gather intelligence about the situation.

They apparently fulfill the mission and come across the home of a prostitute named Rahab. When Jericho soldiers track the men there, Rahab hides them and throws the soldiers off the scent. Because of this act of kindness, the men promise Rahab that they will save her and her household and instruct her to put a scarlet cord outside of her window so they will be able to recognize the house. Because of Rahab's faithfulness, she becomes an ancestor of King David and Jesus himself.

BATTLE OF JERICHO

(Joshua 6)

It is time to begin the conquest! God has promised the land of Canaan to Israel, and Jericho is the first challenge they must face. As Joshua is preparing his battle plan, an angel appears to him and gives him instructions about how the city would be taken. First, the army will march around the city once every day for six days. Seven priests would go ahead of the army with the ark of the covenant and blow trumpets. On the seventh day, the priests and the army would march around the city seven times, and after the seventh round, they were to blow the trumpets and shout. When they did this, the walls crumbled down, and Israel's army was able to walk in and conquer the city. Only Rahab's home was spared.

ACHAN

(Joshua 7)

After Jericho, Israel moves on to the next city, Ai. Joshua and Israel assumed the conquest of this city would be just as easy as Jericho, so Joshua only sent about 3000 men rather than the full army. However, unlike Jericho, the Israelite army was defeated, and they lost 36 men. Reeling from the defeat, Joshua sought the Lord to discover why they had been defeated. God revealed to Joshua that they were defeated because someone in the camp had sinned by taking items from the plunder of Jericho that were forbidden. The people cast lots to discover who it was that took the cursed items. The lots landed on a man named Achan.

Achan had taken some clothes and silver and gold and buried them under his tent. Because of this sin and Achan's lack of repentance, he and his family were stoned. Afterward, the Israelites were able to take the city, Ai successfully.

book of JOSHUA

THE SUN STANDS STILL
(Joshua 10)

Israel had conquered the mighty Canaanite cities of Jericho and Ai and had formed an alliance with the men of the city of Gibeon. Now they advanced toward the city of Jerusalem. Having seen what Israel had done to Jericho and Ai and that Israel had allied with the warriors of Gibeon, the king of Jerusalem was afraid. So he formed an alliance with ten other Canaanite kings to attack Gibeon. Because Joshua had formed an alliance with Gibeon, they asked Joshua for help. Joshua and the army of Israel went to fight with these kings. As they fought, God caused large hailstones to fall on the enemy army, and more were killed from the hail than from the swords of Israel's army.

As the enemy armies were fleeing at the end of the day, Joshua prayed to God to make the sun stand still and prolong the day so that they could continue to pursue and overtake the enemy. God answered Joshua's prayer, and the day was extended by a whole day! It was the first and only 48 hour day in history! Joshua and the army of Israel overtook the kings and destroyed them.

book of JUDGES

DEBORAH

(Judges 4)

After Joshua died, Israel fell into idolatry and wickedness. Because of this, God allowed other nations to come and oppress Israel as punishment according to the covenant He made with them. After several years of foreign oppression, the people would repent and cry out to the Lord. God would then raise up a judge to liberate Israel and lead them. Then once that judge died, the cycle would start all over again. This pattern sums up the book of Judges. In this story, Israel had again turned away from God, so God allowed Jabin, a Canaanite king from Hazor, to oppress Israel. Jabin had a general named Sisera that led a mighty force of chariots of iron.

When Israel cried out to the Lord, God raised up a judge and prophetess named Deborah. Deborah called a man named Barak and told him God's plan to deliver the people. Barak gathered an army of 10,000 men and met Sisera's army and chariots, and God promised that he would deliver Sisera into their hands. However, Barak said he would only go out if Deborah came with him. Deborah agreed to go with him but told him that the glory of destroying Sisera would go to a woman. As promised, Barak's army defeated the army of Sisera, and Sisera fled on foot.

Sisera fled to the tent of an ally of his named Heber and his wife, Jael. Heber was not there, but Jael welcomed him into her tent and offered him water and milk. While he laid down to sleep, Jael pinned him to the ground with a tent peg.

GIDEON

(Judges 6-7)

After Deborah's death, Israel once again turned away from God. So God permitted the Midianites to oppress the people for seven years. After seven years, the people repented and cried out to God, so God raised up a man named Gideon. Gideon was beating wheat in a cave to hide it from the Midianites when an angel appeared to him. The angel told Gideon that God had chosen him to deliver Israel from the Midianites. Gideon was not convinced. He pointed out that he was the youngest son of the most insignificant clan in the most insignificant tribe of Israel. However, God assured him that He would be with him.

Gideon wasn't convinced. He asked for a sign. Gideon told God that he would lay a wool fleece on the ground overnight, and in the morning, if the fleece was wet and the ground was dry, then he would know that God was with him. God did as Gideon asked. Next, Gideon asked God to make the ground wet and the fleece dry. Again, God did as Gideon requested. Now Gideon knew that God was on his side.

Gideon mustered up an army of 22,000 men. However, God told him that was too many people. God didn't want Gideon and the people to feel like they won the victory on their own. So God told Gideon to tell the men whoever was afraid can go home. Twelve thousand men went home. But God told Gideon that there were still too many people! So He told Gideon to tell the men to go get a drink from the brook, and whoever uses their hands to lap the water will remain, and whoever put their tongue to the water will go home. This left Gideon with only 300 men.

When it was time for battle, Gideon instructed the men to arm themselves with jars of clay with torches inside. When Gideon gave the signal, they would blow their trumpets, smash the jars and light the torches, and scream, "A sword for the Lord and for Gideon!" The men did just that, and because they attacked at night and because God caused great confusion in the camp, the Midianite army panicked and began to flee and even fought each other! Gideon had delivered his people.

book of JUDGES

SAMSON

(Judges 13-16)

Once again, Israel had forgotten the Lord. They turned to other gods, so God delivered them to the Philistines. Again, God raised up a judge to deliver them named Samson. Samson was a Nazarite, which meant he was specially consecrated to God. As a part of this special covenant, Samson was not to drink any alcohol or cut his hair. God also gave Samson supernatural strength as a weapon against the Philistines. Samson, however, had his own plans and interests. Samson seemed to prefer Philistine women.

Once, while in the Philistine city of Timnah, Samson came across a woman and wanted to marry her even though such a marriage was forbidden. Nevertheless, Samson insisted, and the marriage took place. At the wedding, Samson told a riddle to the guests and promised 30 linen garments and 30 changes of clothes to anybody that could guess it. After three days, nobody could figure it out, so they went to Samson's wife to convince her to tell them or else they would burn her father's house down. When Samson found out about this, he was enraged, both at the men that threatened his wife and also at his wife for betraying his riddle. He went to a nearby city and killed 30 men and took their garments to give to the wedding guests. His wife was given to another man.

Samson then went on a rampage, burning Philistine fields and attacking Philistine cities. Thus, the Philistines went to the Israelites to convince them to turn him over to them, or else they would exact vengeance on the people. The Israelites agreed, and they turned Samson over to the Philistines, who bound him in ropes and chains. On the way to the Philistine capital of Gaza, the Spirit of the Lord came upon Samson, and he broke out of the ropes and chains and slew 1000 Philistines with a donkey's jawbone.

On another occasion, Samson was in another Philistine city and fell in love with a Philistine woman named Delilah. The Philistine army recruited Delilah to extract the secret of Samson's strength so they could subdue him. So Delilah asked Samson three times about where his strength came from, and three times Samson lied. But she pressured him constantly every day until he finally gave in and told her the secret to his strength rested in his hair. So Delilah cut his hair and called the Philistine soldiers to capture him. Samson was powerless to resist. The Philistines captured him, blinded him, and put him to work at a grinding mill in Gaza.

Finally, the Philistines planned to bring Samson into the main area of the city to flaunt and humiliate him. They brought him in between the pillars of the main hall. At this moment, Samson prayed to God that he would strengthen him to finish his mission and take his revenge on the Philistines. God granted Samson's request, and his strength returned to him. Between the pillars, Samson began to push them and consequently brought down the entire temple. In this act, Samson slew more Philistines in his death than he did in his life.

book of RUTH

BOOK OF RUTH
(Ruth 1-4)

In the era of the judges, there was a famine in Israel. A man named Elimelech from Bethlehem sought to escape the famine and relocated his family to Moab. Elimelech was married to a woman named Naomi, and they had two sons. While in Moab, Elimelech died, leaving Naomi as a widow with two sons. Her sons married Moabite women named Orpah and Ruth. However, soon after, both of the sons also died. Now left destitute, Naomi resolved to return to Bethlehem and instructed her daughters-in-law to return home to their families. Orpah returned, but Ruth refused. She committed to accompany Naomi and take care of her.

Naomi remembered that Elimelech had some relatives in Bethlehem, particularly a wealthy one named Boaz. Ruth volunteered to go to Boaz's fields and glean some of the leftover wheat from the harvest. Boaz noticed her and asked who she was, invited her to lunch, and instructed her to only glean from his fields since Naomi was his relative. When Ruth returned home and told Naomi what had happened, Naomi rejoiced and instructed Ruth to go present herself to Boaz. When he laid down to sleep, Ruth was to go and uncover his feet and lay herself there. This was to present herself to Boaz as a potential spouse, so Boaz could redeem her and Naomi and restore them to status. Boaz acknowledged that he would redeem Ruth and Naomi. However, there was a closer relative that had the first choice.

At a community meeting in the city, later on, Boaz met with the closer relative and cleverly discouraged him from redeeming Ruth, Naomi, and Elimelech's land, leaving him with the option to do so. So Boaz married Ruth, and the couple had a child named Obed. Obed had a child named Jesse, and Jesse had a child named David, who became the greatest king of Israel.

book of
I SAMUEL

GOD SPEAKS
TO
SAMUEL

(1 Samuel 3)

Samuel was a boy dedicated to God at birth and lived at the Tabernacle with the high priest Eli and his family. Now Eli's sons were engaged in wickedness, such as extorting the people bringing sacrifices and sleeping with servant girls in the tabernacle. However, Eli refused to correct his sons about this behavior. One night, a voice came to Samuel in his sleep calling his name. Samuel got up and went to Eli and asked if he had called him. Eli said that he had not called him, so Samuel went back to sleep. A second time the voice came saying, "Samuel." Again, Samuel got up and went to Eli, asking if he had called him. Again Eli responded that he had not. So Samuel went back to bed. A third time the voice called to Samuel, and a third time Samuel went to Eli. At this point, Eli understood that it was God that was calling the boy. He instructed Samuel to go back to bed, and the next time the voice called, he should respond, *"Speak, for your servant hears."*

Samuel followed Eli's instructions and returned to bed. This time, when Samuel heard the voice, he responded as Eli instructed. God then revealed to Samuel that He was going to judge Eli and his sons for their wickedness and that their time was up. With this message, God established Samuel as a prophet and a judge of Israel. Samuel's prophecy eventually came true. Eli's sons were killed in battle with the Philistines, and when Eli heard about it, he also died.

book of
I SAMUEL

SAMUEL ANOINTS SAUL

(1 Samuel 8-10)

Israel wants a king. The elders approach Samuel, saying they want to have a king like all of the other nations. Samuel warns them that this request is an offense to God because God is their king. However, the people insist, and God tells Samuel to find a king according to His instructions.

God sends Samuel to find a man from the tribe of Benjamin named Saul, son of Kish. Saul was tall and handsome, the most handsome man in all of the nation. One day, some of Kish's donkeys went missing, and Kish sent Saul to find them. Saul searched everywhere but could not find the donkeys. Finally, someone told Saul that there was a man of God in the city, and perhaps he could tell him where the donkeys were. Saul went to find the man of God, who turned out to be Samuel. God revealed to Samuel that this was to be the new king. The task now was to convince Saul of that!

After a series of events, Samuel finally anoints Saul as the king of Israel. He then tells him to go near Rachel's tomb, and he will meet two men, and he will find his father's donkeys there. Saul found the donkeys and met the men who took Saul up to a city, and they were possessed by the Spirit of God and began to play music and prophesy. Then Saul was instructed to offer a burnt offering and wait seven days for Samuel to arrive. When Samuel arrived, he called the tribes of Israel together, and they cast lots. The lots singled out the tribe of Benjamin, and eventually the house of Kish, and then Saul himself. But Saul had hidden himself among the people. However, when he stood up, he was a head taller than all of the people. Samuel then presented Saul as the new king of Israel.

SAMUEL ANOINTS DAVID

(1 Samuel 16)

In the first few years of Saul's reign, he did what was right in the sight of the Lord. However, Saul began to be filled with pride and rebellion and began to disobey the commands of Samuel and the Lord. In one instance, before a battle, Samuel instructed Saul to wait until he arrived to offer a sacrifice to the Lord before going into battle. Saul grew impatient because Samuel was delayed and offered the sacrifice himself. This displeased Samuel and God. On another occasion, God commanded Saul to attack the Amalakites and to eradicate every living thing among them. Again, Saul disobeyed and saved the king and some of the animals. After these offenses, God rejected Saul as king.

God then instructed Samuel to go to the town of Bethlehem to the house of Jesse and anoint one of his sons as the next king of Israel. When Samuel arrived, he told Jesse of his mission and called all of his sons together. Samuel saw the oldest son, Eliab, and saw that he was tall and handsome and looked like a king. Surely, this is the one he thought. However, God rebuked Samuel and reminded him that people look at the outward appearance, but the Lord looks at the heart. After going through all of Jesse's sons that were present, God had still not revealed the next king. Samuel asked if Jesse had any other sons. Jesse told him there was one in the fields tending the sheep, but he was just a boy. Samuel instructed Jesse to call him. When David arrived, God told Samuel he was the one, and Saul anointed him as the next king of Israel.

book of I SAMUEL

DAVID
AND
GOLIATH

(1 Samuel 17)

The Philistines have attacked Israel, and they have come with a champion. It was a common feature of ancient warfare to have battles between the best fighters of both armies. The Philistines brought a warrior named Goliath of Gath, a giant standing around nine feet tall. Goliath issued a challenge to Israel for them to present their best warrior for him to fight. If Israel's warriors won, then the Philistines would leave, but if they won, Israel would become their slaves. Nobody in Saul's army, including Saul himself, wanted to face the giant.

All of David's older brothers were a part of Saul's army and had gone to fight the Philistines. One day, Jesse asked David to go to the army's camp and take some food to his brothers and make sure they were ok. When the young David arrived, he heard Goliath's challenge. Goliath had also taken to insulting and cursing Israel's God. This infuriated David. David went to King Saul and declared that he would face the giant. Saul told David he was too young and inexperienced to face a giant warrior like Goliath.

David responded that with the power of God, he had slain lions and bears in the keeping of his father's sheep, and this giant would be no different. Saul gave in but insisted that David wear his armor. But Saul's armor was too big for David. David declared that all he needed was his staff and slingshot. David then went down to a stream and picked up five smooth stones.

Finally, David approached Goliath. Goliath hurled insults and taunts at David and Israel. Goliath began to charge at David. David then grabbed one of the stones out of his bag, placed it in his slingshot, and fired it at the charging giant. The stone hit Goliath in the forehead, where there was an opening in his helmet. Goliath fell to the ground, and David grabbed Goliath's sword and finished the job. Realizing their champion was dead, the Philistine's fled, and Israel's victory was complete.

book of
I SAMUEL

SAUL HUNTS DAVID

(1 Samuel 18-24)

After David slew Goliath, he joined Israel's army and became a great warrior. His fame and prowess on the battlefield began to overshadow Saul's. People were beginning to chant the poem, "Saul has slain his thousands, and David his tens of thousands." This angered Saul, and he became extremely jealous to the point that one day he hurled his spear at David. It became clear to David that Saul wanted him dead, so he fled with the help of David's best friend and Saul's son, Jonathan. David spent years on the run hiding from Saul in the wilderness. While on the run, David accumulated a small army of about 500 outcasts and outlaws that became known as David's "Mighty Men."

After many years of being on the run, Saul believed he had David cornered. He went out to confront David in the wilderness in a cave. Once in the area, Saul stopped to take a nap and get some rest. While he slept, David approached and cut off a piece of Saul's robe. When Saul woke up, David called to him, telling him that he had the opportunity to kill him but that he spared his life. David spared him because Saul was still God's anointed, and David would not raise his hand against him. Seeing that David had the opportunity to kill him but did not, Saul repented of his sins against David, and they agreed to go their separate ways in peace.

book of 2 SAMUEL

DAVID AND MEPHIBOSHETH

(2 Samuel 9)

Years after Saul and Jonathan had died and David was made king over Israel, David asked his servants if there were any members of Saul's family left so he could show kindness to them? His advisors told him there was a son of Jonathan named Mephibosheth who was crippled. David sent for Mephibosheth and told him that because of his love for his father, Jonathan, David would take care of Mephibosheth and his household for all of their days. David did this in honor of Jonathan. And so Mephibosheth, his sons, and his servants were all cared for by David and ate at the king's table.

DAVID AND BATHSHEBA

(2 Samuel 11-12)

During a time of war, David stayed home in Jerusalem rather than leading his men in battle. One day David went out to his roof and saw a woman on another roof bathing as was customary in those times. When David asked about her, his servants told him the woman was named Bathsheba and that she was the wife of one of his soldiers named Uriah. David summoned her anyway and slept with her.

Soon after, Bathsheba sent word to David that she was pregnant. Upon hearing this, David sent for Uriah and summoned him to the palace. David gave him wine and invited him to go spend the night with his wife. However, Uriah refused. If his men were camping in tents under the stars, then he could not go home and be with his wife. So he, too, camped in the courtyard. The next night David tried the same thing but gave him more wine. Even still, Uriah would not go home. David had to act fast. He sent a note with Uriah to take back to Joab, his general, instructing him to put Uriah on the front lines of the hottest part of the battle and then abandon him there so he would be killed. Joab did as instructed, and Uriah was killed. Then David took Bathsheba as his wife.

About a year later, the prophet Nathan came to David. He told him about a rich man that had lots of sheep and flocks. There was also a poor man with one small lamb that he had raised since birth. This lamb was all he had. One day, a traveler came to visit the rich man, and rather than taking a lamb from his own flock, he took the poor man's lamb. Hearing this story, David was enraged. He ordered that the rich man be punished. He should pay the poor man back four times for the lamb he stole. Suddenly, Nathan pointed to David and said, "You are the man!" Nathan recounted to David what he had done to Uriah and Bathsheba and how displeased God was with him. Because of David's sin, David would lose four children violently and was never the same ruler.

book of 2 SAMUEL

ABSALOM'S REBELLION

(2 Samuel 13-18)

David had a son named Absalom, who was very handsome and had long flowing hair. Absalom had certain advisors that convinced him that he could and should be the king. So Absalom began to go to the city gates early in the morning and intercept travelers coming to receive judgment from the king. Absalom would inform them that no one was appointed to hear their complaints but that if he was their judge, everyone would have a voice. By doing this, he won the hearts of the people and even began to win the hearts of the army. David was forced to flee Jerusalem.

Eventually, Absalom and his army pursued David, and David sent his army out to meet them. However, David gave Joab and his other generals the instructions to capture Absalom but not to kill him. However, as the battle progressed, Joab's army prevailed, and Absalom was on the run. As he was fleeing on his mule, he rode under an oak tree with large branches, and his hair got caught in the branches. He was hanging there helpless and unable to free himself. When one of Joab's soldiers reported that Absalom was hanging from the tree, Joab became upset that the soldier didn't strike him down. So Joab took three spears and struck him himself and killed him. When David heard of this, he was furious at Joab and fell into weeping and mourning for Absalom. Joab, however, rebuked David for his excessive mourning. The army had won a great victory, yet David soured the victory with his mourning for the enemy. Joab advised David that if he did not straighten up and encourage the men, the army would lose morale. David did as he was advised, but he never forgave Joab for killing Absalom.

book of I KINGS

SOLOMON BECOMES KING
(1 Kings 1)

In David's old age, he became more concerned about who would be his heir. God had appointed that his son Solomon would be the next king. However, one of David's other sons, Adonijah, sought to claim the throne. Adonijah was spoiled because David failed to discipline him. He accrued a small army of men and had the support of David's former general, Joab. He also had the support of Abiathar, the priest. With this support, Adonijah had Abiathar anoint him king of Israel.

When David heard of this, he was angry, as was Bathsheba, Solomon's mother. David called Nathan the prophet and Zadok, the priest, and Solomon was anointed, king. David then instructed that Solomon be given his mule to ride on throughout the city while the trumpet blew so that the people knew that Solomon was the rightful king. All of those who stood in support of Adonijah left him and went to Solomon.

SOLOMON'S WISDOM
(1 Kings 3)

After David's death, God told Solomon to ask for whatever he wanted, and God would grant it. Rather than asking for riches, glory, or power, Solomon asked for wisdom to lead God's people. Because of this request, God declared that he would give Solomon great wisdom.

Soon after, this wisdom was put to the test. Two women came to Solomon for judgment. Both women had given birth around the same time, but one of the babies died. The mother with the dead child then took the dead baby and switched it with the other woman's baby, making her think that the dead child was hers. The other woman, however, knew that the dead baby was not hers. So the women came to the king. Solomon ordered that a sword be brought to him. He then declared that his solution was to cut the living baby in half and give one half to each woman. When he did this, the real mother interjected and told him just to give the baby to the other woman so that the child would live. Upon seeing this, Solomon gave the child to her, knowing that it was her child because she could not tolerate watching the child die. This was one of the first great displays of Solomon's wisdom.

SOLOMON AND THE QUEEN OF SHEBA
(1 Kings 10)

News of Solomon's fame and wisdom had spread throughout the region. One day, the Queen of the land of Sheba (Ethiopia) came to visit Solomon and see his wisdom for herself. She bombarded him with lots of questions to test his wisdom, and he answered them all to her surprise and elation. She acknowledged that he was indeed the wisest person and was blessed by God.

book of
I KINGS

ELIJAH AND WIDOW OF ZAREPHATH
(1 Kings 17)

Elijah was a prophet called by God to deliver a message to the wicked Israelite king, Ahab, and his wife, Jezebel. Because of Ahab's wickedness, God instructed Elijah to go to Ahab and declare that there would be no rain until Elijah said so. After breaking into the palace and giving this message, Elijah fled into the wilderness. While in the wilderness, God provided for him by having ravens bring him food. Eventually, God guides him to the home of a widow in the land of Zarephath. Upon arriving at the widow's home, he asks for some food. The woman tells him that she only has enough to make a final meal for her and her son, and then they will die. Elijah tells her that if she feeds him instead, God will greatly bless her. She takes a step of faith and prepares some bread for Elijah. After Elijah had eaten, God miraculously filled the woman's jars of flour and oil to overflowing. God would continue to refill the woman's supply until the drought was over because of her faithfulness.

Sometime later, the woman's son died. Elijah went into the child and laid on top of him, and prayed. Elijah, through the power of God, brought the child back to life. After all these things, Elijah left the widow's home to confront Ahab once again.

SHOWDOWN ON MT CARMEL
(1 Kings 18)

Three years after Elijah's decree of no rain, no rain had fallen in Israel. God commanded Elijah to confront Ahab again. Elijah challenged Ahab and the prophets of Baal to join him on Mt. Carmel. There, they would offer sacrifices, and each would pray to their respective gods, and whichever responded with fire would be God. So Ahab and 450 prophets of Baal gathered on the mountain and prepared their sacrifices. Then they danced and chanted and cut themselves, begging for Baal to answer. They did this for several hours, and Elijah began to taunt them. Nothing happened.

Finally, Elijah built his altar and placed the animal on the altar. Elijah then prayed to God, and God responded with fire so hot that it not only consumed the sacrifice but also the altar itself. Now it was known that Jehovah was God! Elijah then had all of the prophets of Baal killed and prayed for rain to return to Israel.

book of
2 KINGS

ELIJAH TAKEN TO HEAVEN
(2 Kings 2)

God has told Elijah that he will be taken alive up to heaven. God had previously instructed Elijah to find his replacement who is named Elisha. Now, the time is near. Elijah tells Elisha to ask for anything he wants, and if God wills, he will grant it. Elisha asks for a double portion of the spirit of Elijah. Elijah tells him that if he sees him being taken up to heaven that the double portion would fall on him.

Soon after, the two prophets approach the river Jordan. Elijah then removes his cloak and places it in the river, and it parts for him and Elisha, and they cross over. Once they crossed over, chariots of fire descended from heaven and took Elijah. After seeing this, Elisha goes back to the Jordan with Elijah's cloak. He rolls up the cloak and places it in the river, and the water again parts for him, declaring to everyone that Elisha is now the prophet of Israel.

NAAMAN'S LEPROSY
(2 Kings 5)

There was a commander in the Syrian army named Naaman. Naaman had come down with a deadly disease called leprosy. Now Naaman had an Israelite servant girl. When the girl saw how her master was suffering, she told them of a prophet in Israel that could cure him of his leprosy.

Naaman sent word to the king of Syria about what his servant girl had said, and the king sent word to the king of Israel to expect Naaman's arrival. The king of Israel sent word to Elisha, and Elisha agreed to see him.

When Naaman arrived at Elisha's house, Elisha would not come out but sent his servant out to greet Naaman instead. The servant instructed Naaman that Elisha commanded him to go and wash in the river Jordan seven times, and then he would be cured. Naaman was furious! He came all that way for Elisha to not even greet him in person and then to ask him to bathe in one of the dirtiest bodies of water in the land! So Naaman left to return to Syria. However, one of Naaman's servants advised him to do as Elisha said. After all, what could it hurt? So Naaman turned back and went to the river. He dipped down one time—nothing happened. Twice, and still nothing. Three, four, five, six —still nothing. Finally, after the seventh time, Naaman's leprosy was cured, and he was clean.

Naaman was elated! He returned to Elisha to thank him and to offer him the money and gifts that he had brought. However, Elisha refused the money and gifts because he could not take payment for the works of God. Naaman also committed to worship the God of Israel from that point on, and he went on his way. Elisha's servant followed Naaman so that he could receive the money and gifts that Naaman had brought. However, when he returned, Elisha knew what he had done. Because of his greed, Naaman's leprosy was transferred to him.

HEZEKIAH'S LIFE SPARED
(2 Kings 20)

King Hezekiah was the king of Judah. He was one of the few kings that served God and worshipped him, and kept the nation on God's path. However, Hezekiah came down with a severe illness. Isaiah, the prophet, told him that he was not going to recover from it. Hezekiah was greatly grieved and pleaded with the Lord for his life. God heard Hezekiah's prayer and told Isaiah to turn back and tell him that He would give him fifteen more years. Hezekiah then asked Isaiah what would be God's sign that he would be healed? Isaiah asked him whether he wanted God to move the shadow of the sundial forward ten steps or back ten steps. Hezekiah said back ten steps. So God turned the sundial back ten steps, which means he turned time back ten minutes.

book of 2 KINGS

ISRAEL AND JUDAH TAKEN CAPTIVE

(2 Kings 17; 25)

After the time of Solomon, the kingdom of Israel was divided into Northern (Israel) and Southern (Judah) kingdoms. None of the kings of the northern kingdom of Israel served the Lord. They all went after idols, led the people astray, and practiced wickedness. God sent prophet after prophet after prophet to the people to warn them of God's judgment and try to bring them back. But the kings and the people rejected the prophets and even killed some of them. Because of their breaking of the covenant God had made with them, God permitted the Assyrian empire to conquer the northern kingdom of Israel, and it was destroyed in 722 B.C.

Like Israel, the southern kingdom of Judah also broke God's covenant. However, because of a few good kings that led Judah in a righteous direction, their judgment was delayed. God also sent many prophets to Judah. Judah had good kings such as Asa, Josiah, and Hezekiah. However, it was too little too late. God's judgment had been pronounced. God allowed the Babylonian empire to conquer Judah in 586 B.C. Yet, God promised that He would restore the people after 70 years.

book of NEHEMIAH

NEHEMIAH REBUILDS THE WALLS OF JERUSALEM

(1 Kings 17)

Nehemiah was part of those who had been taken in the Babylonian captivity. God put in his heart the desire to return to Jerusalem and rebuild the city's walls that had been destroyed One day, Nehemiah approached king Artaxerxes (the Persian empire had conquered Babylon by this point) and asked him permission to return to Jerusalem to rebuild the walls. Xerxes agreed. So Nehemiah returned to Jerusalem and set about rebuilding the wall.

There were two men named Sanballat and Tobiah who opposed Nehemiah and the people from rebuilding the walls and resorted to attacks against the builders. So Nehemiah assigned a portion of the men to build and another portion to carry swords, spears, shields, and armor. When Sanballat and Tobiah saw that Israel had armed themselves, they left them alone to build. Eventually, Nehemiah finished the walls, and they were ready when Cyrus would later release Judah to return to the land.

STORY OF ESTHER

In the time of Judah's captivity during the reign of Xerxes in Persia, Xerxes was on the hunt for a new queen. His former queen Vashti refused to expose herself to the king and his guests, and she was banished. So Xerxes issued a decree that all virgin girls in the kingdom come and present themselves to him so he could select a new queen.

Now there was a Jewish man named Mordecai who had a cousin named Hadassah who was very beautiful. Upon hearing the king's decree, Mordecai instructed Hadassah to go by a Persian name, Esther, and not to tell the king that she was Jewish. So Esther was taken and spent a year being prepared to meet with the king. After going in to the king, Xerxes decided that she would be his new queen.

There was an advisor to Xerxes named Haman. Xerxes made Haman second in command in the empire and declared that when Haman passed by, they needed to bow in reverence. But whenever Haman passed by Mordecai, he refused to bow. Because of this, Haman hated Mordecai and all of the Jews. So he hatched a plot to destroy all of the Jews throughout the Persian empire. He convinced the king to decree one day when all of the Jews would be killed. When Mordecai heard of this, he went into a period of mourning. When Esther saw him mourning, she asked why, and he told her what the king had decreed. He then told Esther to go present herself to the king and reveal herself to him and plead with him to save their people. Esther knew that to go into the king uninvited was a death sentence. But Mordecai convinced her, saying, "Perhaps you were made queen for such a time as this."

So Esther went to the king, and he had mercy on her and asked for her request. She requested that he and Haman attend a series of banquets, and he agreed. On the third banquet, she revealed to king Haman's plot against the Jews and that she was Jewish. Upon hearing this, the king had Haman hanged on the gallows Haman had built for Mordecai. While the king could not reverse his decree, he made another decree enabling the Jews to fight back against anybody that rose against them. The Jews were saved because of Esther's courage and faithfulness.

WISDOM
Books

JOB

Job was a righteous non-Israelite man in the land of Uz. He served the One True God. God blessed him with lots of flocks, herds, riches, and many children. When Job's children would hold a feast, Job would offer sacrifice in the mornings in case his children had sinned in their partying.

One day, a council of divine beings gathered in heaven, and Satan presented himself as the representative of earth. God asked Satan where he was coming from, and Satan replied he was wandering on the earth, implying he was seeking someone to whom he could bring mischief. God asked Satan if he had considered his servant Job, who was righteous and blameless. Satan asserted that the only reason that Job serves God is because God has protected him and blessed him. However, if God would remove his protection and allow Satan to afflict him, Job would curse God. God allowed Satan to attack Job, but not his body.

One day, one of Job's servants came to tell him that there was a raid from a band of Sabeans, and they killed Job's servants that were attending his oxen and donkeys. Then, another servant came and told Job that fire came down from heaven and burned up his flocks of sheep and the servants that attended them. Finally, another servant came and told Job that his children were gathered in the oldest brother's house to eat, and a great wind came and destroyed the house and all his children with it. Hearing this, Job ripped his clothes and shaved his head in mourning. However, he did not curse God.

After this, Satan returned to God, and God again raised Job's case before him, pointing out that Job had not cursed God. Satan again asserted that the only reason Job had not yet cursed God was because God would not allow him to strike his body. God then agreed to allow Satan to attack Job's body but forbade him from killing him. So Satan afflicted Job with terrible sores and boils all over his body. For relief, Job would scrape himself with broken pottery.

Job would cry out to God for answers, but God would not respond. One day, three of Job's friends—Eliphaz, Bildad, and Zophar arrived to encourage Job. However, when they saw Job's misery, they sat silently for three days. When they finally started speaking, they blamed Job for his condition, suggesting that this was happening because he had sinned. However, Job knew he was innocent and only wanted God to talk to him.

God did finally respond to Job and asserted his sovereignty before Job. At this, Job repented and humbled himself. God restored Job's health, his flocks, and herds and gave him ten more children. God never revealed to Job why these afflictions came on him.

PROPHETIC Books

ISAIAH

(Isaiah 20)

God occasionally asked prophets to do strange things to make a point. One day, God commanded the prophet Isaiah to wander naked for three years. This was to illustrate a prophecy that God would allow the Assyrians to cause the Egyptians to wander naked and barefoot through their conquest. Isaiah's ministry lasted forty years in the nation of Judah.

JEREMIAH

(Jeremiah 1)

Jeremiah was from a family of priests. One day, while he was still a small boy, God spoke to Jeremiah and told him that he would appoint him as a prophet to Judah and to the nations. God told him that he would face resistance but that He would be with him. God touched Jeremiah's lips and put His message in his mouth. Jeremiah's ministry would be focused on the nation of Judah for forty years.

JEREMIAH THROWN INTO WELL

(Jeremiah 38)

God gave Jeremiah a message to proclaim to the people saying that the Babylonians were coming to destroy Jerusalem. Furthermore, he told them that whoever stayed in the city would die and whoever went out to the Babylonians and surrendered would be spared. The city officials didn't like this message of Jeremiah encouraging the people to surrender, so they placed him in an empty well to silence him.

Eventually, an Ethiopian eunuch named Ebed-Melech rescued Jeremiah, and Jeremiah returned to the king and pronounced another judgment.

EZEKIEL

(Ezekiel 1)

God called Ezekiel to a very particular prophetic ministry. Ezekiel ministered to the Jews during the time of the Babylonian exile. Ezekiel's prophecies contained lots of symbols and apocalyptic images that were unique among the ancient Israelite prophets. One of Ezekiel's most famous visions showed four unidentified creatures and four wheels that accompanied them. These seemed to be large wheel-like structures, some of them with more wheels inside of them. Ezekiel saw that the spirit of the creatures was inside the wheels.

Jewish and Christian scholars and theologians have debated what these wheels meant for centuries with no solid consensus. The answer seems to depend on who is asking the question!

book of DANIEL

DANIEL REFUSES THE KING'S FOOD
(Daniel 1)

During the time of the Babylonian conquest of Jerusalem, the Babylonian king, Nebuchadnezzar, took captives back to Babylon. Four of the captives he took were four boys named Daniel, Azariah, Hananiah, and Mischael. The king put them in training to be officials in his court and changed their names to names based on the Babylonian gods—Belteshazzar, Abednego, Shadrach, and Meschach. In the course of their training, the king provided food for them to eat that did not align with Israelite kosher laws as expressed in the Torah. So Daniel and his friends refused to eat the king's food and asked for a diet of water and vegetables instead. The eunuch in charge of them was hesitant, thinking they would wither away. However, Daniel put forward a challenge asking them to give him ten days with this diet and that they would be healthier than the other Babylonian children in training. Indeed, after ten days, Daniel and his friends were visibly healthier than the others.

FIERY FURNACE
(Daniel 3)

One day, King Nebuchadnezzar decided to construct a massive golden statue of himself and commanded the kingdom to gather and bow before it. Anyone that did not bow would be cast into a fiery furnace. However, there were at least three in the kingdom that would refuse to bow—Shadrach, Meshach, and Abednego. When the kingdom gathered in the valley and the music played, everyone bowed except for the three Hebrew boys.

When the king's officials told him, the king summoned the three Hebrews. He gave them another chance to bow before the image, but they again refused because they could only bow before God. Nebuchadnezzar was furious and told his officials to make the fire seven times hotter and then throw the three men in. They did as they were commanded and made the fire hotter. The fire was so hot that when the guards went to throw Shadrach, Meshach, and Abednego in, it swallowed them up as well! Nebuchadnezzar watched with satisfaction as the men were thrown in. However, as he continued to watch, he noticed a fourth person in the fire. He confirmed with his advisors that he only threw three people in and then noted that there was a fourth person in the furnace who looked like a son of the gods! Nebuchadnezzar had the men removed from the furnace and noted that they were not burned at all and did not even smell like smoke. Because of this mighty miracle, Nebuchadnezzar committed to worship the God of Israel.

HANDWRITING ON THE WALL
(Daniel 5)

After Nebuchadnezzar died, his son, Belshazzar, became king of Babylon. One day, Belshazzar had a large feast with thousands of his subjects and officials. During the feast, Belshazzar commanded that the sacred artifacts and cups from the temple in Jerusalem be brought out and used while they praised the gods of gold, silver, and bronze.

Suddenly, a hand appeared and wrote something on the wall in a foreign language. The king called his wise men and magicians to interpret, but none of them could. The king promised anyone who could interpret the message a high position in the kingdom as well as riches, but still, no one could read it. Finally, the queen suggested the king call one of his father's former advisors—a Hebrew named Daniel. When Daniel arrived, he interpreted the message for the king. The hand of God wrote that the days of the kingdom of Babylon were numbered, and it was found lacking in the balances of judgments. Finally, Daniel said that Babylon would be conquered and divided between the kings of the Medes and the Persians. It happened that exact night, just as Daniel had prophesied.

book of DANIEL

DANIEL

IN

LION'S DEN

(Daniel 6)

Darius the Mede was now king of Persia, and Daniel was one of his top advisors and officials in the kingdom. Because of this, some of the otherwise men became jealous of Daniel and tried to find a way to discredit and destroy him. However, because Daniel was righteous, they could find no fault in him. So they proposed to the king that he issue a decree that a day be set aside for the worship of Darius. On this day, no one would be permitted to worship any other deity except Darius, and anyone caught worshipping another god would be cast in the lion's den. They did this knowing that Daniel prayed by his window toward Jerusalem three times a day.

Sure enough, Daniel went to his window to pray, and the advisors turned him in. Daniel was cast into the lion's den, much to Darius' dismay because he loved Daniel. As Daniel was in the den, an angel shut the lion's mouths and made them as docile as house cats. In the morning, Darius went to the lion's den and called out to Daniel. Daniel was alive! Darius ordered Daniel be removed and his accusers be thrown in in his place. Then Darius decreed that everyone should worship Daniel's God.

book of HOSEA

JONAH

Jonah was a prophet of God to the northern kingdom of Israel. However, one day, God spoke to Jonah and instructed him to go to the Assyrian city of Nineveh and to warn them of coming judgment if they did not turn from their wicked ways and repent. But Jonah did not want to preach to Nineveh because the Assyrians were cruel and violent and enemies of God's people. So instead of going to Nineveh, Jonah booked passage to a city named Tarshish in the opposite direction. While on the ship, God sent a great storm upon the ship. The storm was so heavy that everyone thought the ship would sink. Jonah knew, however, that God had sent the storm because of his disobedience. So Jonah asked the men to throw him overboard, and the storm would go away. The crew obliged and threw Jonah into the sea. While in the sea, God prepared a great fish to save Jonah. Jonah stayed in the belly of the fish for three days and nights.

While inside the fish, Jonah prayed to God and repented of his sin, and the fish deposited Jonah on dry land again. Jonah then made his way to Nineveh. Jonah preached the message God had given him in Nineveh, and the people repented! However, rather than being happy that his preaching was received, Jonah was furious. He wanted God to punish Nineveh. God caused a vine to grow overnight to give Jonah shade during the day. However, the vine shriveled in the course of a day. Jonah again got very upset and asked God to let him die. God then spoke to Jonah and rebuked him for being upset that God had destroyed this vine that God created and then decided to take away. Why should God save the vine but not save the city of Nineveh with thousands of people in it?

HOSEA AND GOME

(Hosea 1, 3)

Hosea was called as a prophet to the northern kingdom of Israel before it was destroyed by Assyria in 722 B.C. Like Isaiah, God used Hosea's actual life as an object lesson. God told Hosea to go marry a prostitute to illustrate that Israel had prostituted herself out to idols. So Hosea married a woman named Gomer, and they had a son named Jezreel. God instructed them to name him Jezreel as a prophecy against the land of Jezreel. Next, Hosea and Gomer had a daughter, and God instructed them to name her Lo-ruhama, which meant "No Mercy," because God would not have mercy on Israel. Their next child would be called Lo-Ammi, which meant "not my people."

Eventually, Gomer went back to her profession, much to Hosea's disgrace. God then instructed him to go find her and bring her home. So Hosea went and found her and bought her back. This was for God to illustrate that in spite of Israel's unfaithfulness, He would redeem her and bring her back to Him.

I HAVE TOLD YOU THESE THINGS,

so that in me you may have peace.

In this world you will have trouble. But take heart! I have overcome the world.

John 16:33

new

testament

book of MATTHEW

MAGI VISIT JESUS

(Matthew 2:1-12)

After being born in Bethlehem, magi, or wise men, from the east, came to find Jesus. Sometime earlier, a star appeared in the heavens. The magi, who were astrologers, saw the star and somehow knew it represented the birth of a new king. So they set out to find the child. The star led them to the land of Judea, so they stopped in Jerusalem to inquire of King Herod, the location of the child. Herod did not know, but his advisors told them that the Messiah was to be born in Bethlehem based on the scriptures. So the magi set out for Bethlehem. However, Herod, hearing that a new king was born, set out to destroy the child.

So the wise men made their way to Bethlehem and found the child and his parents. When they found him, they bowed down and worshipped him. They brought gifts of gold, frankincense, and myrrh. The text does not say there were three wise men. That tradition comes from the three gifts. Before they left to return to their land, an angel instructed them not to go back to Herod in Jerusalem but to take another route.

book of MATTHEW

JESUS HEALS CENTURION'S SERVANT

(Matthew 8:5-13)

As Jesus entered the Galilean town of Capernaum, a Roman centurion came to ask him to heal his servant, who was very sick. Jesus agreed to heal him and asked the centurion to show him to his house. But the centurion told Jesus he did not need to come to his house. As a person with authority, the centurion knew that when he issued an order that his men will carry it out. In the same way, he said to Jesus if he just gives the word, he knew that his servant would be healed. Hearing this, Jesus marveled at his faith. He said he hadn't seen faith like this in all of Israel! Jesus told the centurion to go in peace because his servant was healed.

book of MATHEW

TRANSFIGURATION

(Matthew 17:1-13)

One day, Jesus called three disciples, Peter, James, and John, and took them up with him on a mountain. While on the mountain, Jesus transforms before them into something like a spiritual being—radiating with light. Suddenly, both Moses and Elijah appeared to them and were talking to Jesus. Seeing this, Peter suggested they set up a few tents: one for Jesus, one for Moses, and one for Elijah. While he was saying this, a voice from heaven declared, "This is my beloved Son, in whom I am well pleased." After this, Moses and Elijah disappeared, and the light from Jesus faded. He instructed his disciples not to tell anyone what they had seen and heard.

JESUS CLEANSES THE TEMPLE

(Matthew 21:12-17)

When Jesus arrived in Jerusalem and made his way to the temple, he found a large marketplace. People were exchanging goods and buying and selling doves and other animals for sacrifice and exploiting the poor. This angered Jesus, and he began to overturn the money changer's tables. Then he said, "It is written, 'My house shall be called a house of prayer,' but you have made it a den of thieves!" This act greatly angered the religious leaders, and they resolved even more to eliminate him.

book of MARK

JOHN THE BAPTIST PREPARES THE WAY

(Mark 1:1-11)

A man named John appeared in Judea and began preaching and calling the people to repentance. His message was to prepare the hearts and minds of the people for the coming of the Messiah. He began to baptize people in the river Jordan as a symbol of their repentance. John wore clothes made of camel's hair and ate locusts and honey, and lived in the wilderness.

book of MARK

JESUS CASTS OUT DEMONS

(Mark 1:21-28)

One Sabbath, Jesus was teaching in the synagogue when a demon-possessed man appeared. The demon in the man began to yell out that he knew who Jesus was—the Son of God. Jesus commanded him to be quiet and then commanded the demon to come out of the man. At seeing this, the people wondered who this man was that even had authority over demons!

book of MARK

JESUS RAISES JAIRUS' DAUGHTER AND HEALS WOMAN WITH ISSUE OF BLOOD

(Mark 5:21-43)

While in Capernaum, a synagogue leader named Jairus had a daughter that became very sick. When he heard Jesus was in town, he approached him to ask for healing. Jesus agreed and began to make his way to Jairus' house.

On the way, a woman that had an issue of menstrual bleeding for twelve years made her way through the crowds and barely managed to grab the hem of Jesus' robe, and she was immediately healed.

Suddenly, Jesus stopped. "Who touched me?" he asked. Hearing this question, his disciples responded that everybody was touching him because they're in a crowd of people. Jesus, however, perceived that spiritual power had left him. The woman then came forward and presented herself and her case to Jesus. Jesus praised her for her faith and sent her on her way.

Meanwhile, a servant from Jairus' house came and relayed that his daughter had died, so they didn't need to bother Jesus any further. Overhearing what they were saying, Jesus told them to simply believe. Jesus still accompanied them to the house and instructed Peter, James, and John to join him. As they entered, women were wailing loudly as was customary. However, Jesus told them to be quiet because the girl was not dead, only sleeping. Hearing this, the crowd mocked Jesus. Jesus told everybody to go outside except for Peter, James, and John and then went into the girl's room. Jesus took her by the hand and said in Aramaic, "Talitha cumi," which means "little girl, I say to you, arise." Immediately the girl got up and began walking around! The crowd was amazed.

book of MARK

JESUS FEEDS FIVE THOUSAND

(Mark 6:30-44)

Jesus and his disciples got on a boat to get some quiet rest time, but the crowds saw them and began to gather to hear Jesus teach. So Jesus taught the crowds until it was late and the people didn't have anything to eat. When the disciples told Jesus that many of the people were beginning to get restless and hungry, Jesus told them to give them something to eat. But there were over 5,000 people in the crowd! How could they feed all those people? So, Jesus had them go through the crowd and see if anybody had any food. They came back and reported that they were only able to find five loaves of bread and two fish.

Jesus commanded the crowd to gather into groups of hundreds and fifties and to sit down. Then he took the bread and fish, prayed and blessed them, and gave them to the disciples to give to the people. Miraculously, the food never ran out, and there was enough for everyone to eat.

book of MARK

JESUS WALKS on WATER

(Mark 6:45-52)

After the miracle of the feeding of the 5,000, Jesus and his disciples got on a boat and crossed the sea to the other side, where Jesus went on a mountain to pray. When he came down, he began to walk on the sea. Still in the boat, the disciples saw a figure walking on the water, and at first thought, it was a ghost. Then Jesus called out to them and told them not to be afraid. Yet, the disciples were still afraid and marveled at what they saw.

book of LUKE

JESUS' BIRTH ANNOUNCED TO SHEPHERDS
(Luke 2:8-21)

After Jesus was born, some shepherds were tending their flocks when suddenly, an angel appeared to them. The angel told them not to be afraid but that a child was born that would be Christ the Lord. The angel then told them that they would find the child wrapped in swaddling clothes in a manager. Suddenly, a multitude of angels appeared and began to sing: "Glory to God in the highest."

The shepherds made their way into Bethlehem and found Mary, Joseph, and the child, and they worshipped him.

JESUS LOST IN JERUSALEM
(Luke 2:41-52)

When Jesus was twelve years old, he and his parents made their way to Jerusalem to celebrate Passover. When they were ready to return home, Mary and Joseph started the journey with their caravan but didn't realize Jesus wasn't with them. Jesus stayed behind in the temple and had begun teaching.

When Mary and Joseph realized Jesus was not with them, they turned back and looked for him for three days. Finally, they found him at the temple. They asked why he had done this to them. He responded, "Did you not know I must be about my Father's business?" His parents were amazed and did not understand what he was saying.

GOOD SAMARITAN
(Luke 10:25-37)

One day, a lawyer challenged Jesus asking him the question, "Who is my neighbor?" Jesus responded by telling a parable. A man was traveling the perilous road from Jerusalem to Jericho. On the road, the man was beaten and robbed and left for dead. Shortly after, a priest passed by. He saw the man on the side of the road but passed on the other side. Next, a Levite (a temple worker) passed by and saw the man, but he too kept going. Finally, a Samaritan passed by. Samaritans and Jews did not get along and hated each other. Nevertheless, the Samaritan stopped, picked the man up and set him on his animal, and tended to his wounds. Then he took him to the nearest inn and paid for his meals and lodging until he recovered.

So Jesus asked the lawyer who was a neighbor to the man on the road? "The one who showed mercy on him," the lawyer responded. Jesus told the man if he did the same, he would receive eternal life.

book of LUKE

PRODIGAL SON

(Luke 15:11-32)

Religious leaders were complaining that Jesus spent too much time with sinners. So Jesus told this parable. A man had two sons, and the younger son wanted his share of his inheritance. So the father divided his property between his sons, and the younger son took his share and went to the city where he engaged in reckless living. Eventually, his money ran out, and then a famine came on the land. Desperate for food and shelter, the son found a job with a pig farmer feeding the pigs, which was forbidden for a Jew. When the pigs' food began to look good to him, he came to his senses and decided to return home.

While he was on the road, still a long way off, the father saw him and ran out to meet him and hugged and kissed him. The son told his father that he was a sinner and not worthy of being called his son and asked if he would take him in as a servant. But the father ordered that robes be put on him, a ring be put on him, and the fattened calf be killed in preparation for a feast in his honor. For his son was dead and was alive again; he was lost but now was found.

When the older brother heard feasting, he asked what was going on. A servant told him that his brother had returned after wasting all of his inheritance. The older brother was furious and refused to go join the party. When the father heard this, he came out to talk to him. The older brother lashed out at the father that he had served him faithfully for many years and never asked for anything and never received anything for his troubles. But when his brother returns after wasting his inheritance on partying and women, they kill the fattened calf for him and celebrate. The father responded that he is always with him, but his brother was dead and is alive again; he was lost, but now is found.

Jesus told this story to illustrate to his critics that God will welcome any one of his children into his kingdom that wants to come home.

JESUS AND ZACCHAEUS

(Luke 19:1-10)

Jesus was passing through Jericho on the way to Jerusalem. As he passed through, a tax collector named Zacchaeus came to see him. As a tax collector for the Roman empire, Zacchaeus was very rich and also hated by his people. Zacchaeus was also very short and could not see above the crowd. So he climbed on a nearby sycamore tree to see Jesus. When Jesus saw him, he stopped and called out to him to come down so he could go to his house. Zacchaeus came down and escorted Jesus and his disciples to his house.

While Jesus was at his house, Zacchaeus declared that he would return everything he had stolen and would repay those he defrauded four times over. Jesus declared that now salvation had come to his house.

book of JOHN

JESUS TURNS WATER INTO WINE

(John 2:1-12)

In Galilee, Jesus attended a wedding in a town called Cana. While he was there, the host ran out of wine for the guests. This would be a significant disgrace in that time period and culture. So Mary, Jesus' mother, asked Jesus to help. Jesus asked her what she wanted him to do and told her it wasn't yet his time. Nonetheless, Mary told the servants to do as Jesus instructed. There were six jars of water nearby, so Jesus told them to take the jars and fill them with water. After they filled the jars, Jesus instructed them to pour it into a cup and give it to the master of the ceremony. Upon tasting the water that had now become wine, he declared that usually, people put out the best wine first, but this host has saved the best for last! This was Jesus' first miracle.

WOMAN AT THE WELL

(John 4:1-45)

Jesus and his disciples were passing through Samaria, and they came to the well that Jacob dug. The disciples went into the city to get food and provisions, and Jesus stayed by the well. While there, a Samaritan woman came by to draw water. Jesus asked the woman for a drink. The woman was surprised that Jesus, a Jew, would ask her, a Samaritan, for a drink. Jesus told her if she knew who was asking her for a drink, she would be asking him for a drink of living water. Jesus then tells her that if she were to drink this living water, she would never be thirsty again.

At this, the woman asks where she can get some. Jesus tells her to go get her husband, and he will tell her. The woman replies that she doesn't have a husband. Tells her she's correct because she has had five husbands. The woman was astonished that Jesus knew the inner details of her life. She ran back to her village and told everyone what had happened. Soon the whole village came out to see him, and Jesus gained many followers

book of JOHN

JESUS HEALS BY A POOL

(John 5:1-17)

Jesus and his followers were in Jerusalem to celebrate another festival, and they found themselves by a pool called Bethsaida on the Sabbath. The people believed that angels would visit the pool and cause ripples in the water. When the ripples began, the sick would try to get into the pool before the ripples went away, believing they would be healed.

On the day Jesus was by the pool, a certain paralyzed man had been by the pool for 38 years, and no one ever helped him into the pool. When Jesus saw him, he asked him if he wanted to be healed. The man said yes. Jesus told him to pick up his bed and walk. The man was immediately healed and began to praise God.

The religious leaders, seeing that the man had been healed on the Sabbath, began to question him. The man told them everything that had happened and that Jesus had healed him. This increased the leader's hatred for him.

JESUS HEALS A MAN BORN BLIND

(John 9:1-41)

One day, Jesus and his disciples passed by a man that had been born blind. The disciples asked him why the man had been born blind: was it because of his sin or his parents' sin? This was the way disability was viewed in those days. Jesus responded that the man's condition was neither his fault nor the fault of his parents, but so that God would be glorified. Jesus then approached the man, spit on the ground to make mud, and put it on his eyes. Then Jesus told him to go wash them off in a pool named Siloam. The man went and washed and instantly received his sight. The man left and told others what had happened.

When the religious leaders heard what had happened and that it happened again on the Sabbath, they brought the man in for questioning. The man told them everything that happened and verified that it was Jesus who healed him. When the Pharisees told him to give glory to God and not Jesus for his healing, he refused. All he knew was that Jesus healed him. Because he wouldn't recant, he and his parents were cast out of the synagogue. Later the man ran into Jesus and confirmed his faith.

book of JOHN

JESUS RESURRECTS LAZARUS

(John 11:1-44)

Jesus had some friends named Mary, Martha, and Lazarus that lived in Bethany—a small town outside of Jerusalem. Mary was the one who, in another story, anointed Jesus' feet and washed them with her tears and hair. One day, Lazarus became very ill, so the sisters sent for Jesus. A messenger found Jesus and told him about Lazarus' condition. However, Jesus waited two days before heading to Bethany. By the time he got there, Lazarus had been dead for four days.

When he arrived, Martha came out to meet him and told him that if he had been there, Lazarus would not be dead. Jesus reminded Martha that Lazarus would live again in the resurrection on Judgment Day and that he was the resurrection and the life. He then sent for Mary, and she came to him and said the same thing as Martha. Seeing her and the other people gathered weeping, he began to weep. Then he asked for the location of Lazarus' tomb. So they took him to it.

When they arrived at the tomb, Jesus instructed them to roll away the stone that sealed the tomb. Martha objected, saying that Lazarus had been dead four days and would surely have begun decomposing and causing an odor by now. Jesus insisted. Once the stone was rolled away, Jesus prayed to his Father and then summoned Lazarus to come out of the tomb. Lazarus walked out, still wrapped in his burial linens. Because of this miracle, the Pharisees sought out a way to kill Jesus.

book of ACTS

PENTECOST

(Acts 2:1-41)

After Jesus' death and resurrection, Jesus spent about 40 days with the disciples and all of his other followers and then ascended up to heaven. However, Jesus told them that when he goes, the Holy Spirit will come down and dwell with them to give them power. He instructed them to wait in Jerusalem for the coming of the Spirit.

About 50 days after Jesus' resurrection, during the feast of Pentecost, about 120 disciples were gathered together when the Holy Spirit descended on them in the form of tongues of fire above their heads. Suddenly, they were able to speak and understand various languages so that everyone understood what they were saying in their own language.

Emboldened by this new power, Peter went to the temple square and began to preach to those gathered. He preached such a powerful sermon that 1,000 people were baptized that day.

CONVERSION OF SAUL

(Acts 9:1-19)

There was a man named Saul of Tarsus who was an enemy of the young Christian movement. Saul was a Pharisee and was very zealous for the law of God. When the religious leaders decided it was necessary to stone the deacon Stephen, the first Christian martyr, Saul held the coats of those who were stoning him. After Stephen's stoning, Saul began to persecute the church in Jerusalem. Eventually, he received authority to carry his persecutions to those Christians who had fled to Damascus.

While on the way to Damascus, a bright, blinding light appeared and knocked Saul off of his horse. Then a voice spoke and said, "Saul, Saul, why are you persecuting me?" Saul asked who it was who was speaking, and the voice responded that it was Jesus. Jesus then instructed Saul to continue into the city, and he would be told what to do. Saul rose to follow the instructions, but he was struck blind by the encounter.

In Damascus, there was a believer named Ananias who received a vision from Christ instructing him to find Saul, heal him, and baptize him. However, Ananias was afraid because Saul was an enemy of the church. But Jesus told him to proceed because Saul would be his apostle to the gentiles. When Ananias came to the home where Saul was staying, he healed him of his blindness and baptized him. Immediately, Saul began to preach.

PETER FREED FROM PRISON

(Acts 12:1-19)

Herod Agrippa, the Roman-appointed king over Judea, captured James, son of Zebedee and Peter. James was executed, and Peter was imprisoned, soon to be executed. While he was in prison, an angel appeared to him and told him to get up and follow him. The angel led him past the guards, past the prison gates, and out of the prison altogether. When Peter realized this was real and not a vision, he went to Mary, the mother of John Mark's house, where some of the other believers were gathered.

When he got to the door, he knocked, and a servant girl named Rhoda came to the door. When she recognized Peter's voice, she was excited, but everyone else said there was no way it could be Peter! But Peter kept knocking until they opened the door, and everyone was amazed and praised God.

book of ACTS

PAUL AND SILAS FREED FROM PRISON

(Acts 16:16-40)

Paul and Silas were on a missionary expedition in Philippi in Macedonia. While there, they encountered a slave girl who was a soothsayer and began following them around, declaring them to be servants of God. She followed them day and night for several days until Paul became annoyed and cast the spirit out of her. When her masters learned what had happened and that they could no longer profit off of her fortune-telling, they became enraged and brought them before the authorities. A great riot broke out, and Paul and Silas were beaten and put in prison.

While in prison, Paul and Silas began to sing songs of praise to God. While they were singing, a great earthquake shook the prison and opened the cell doors, freeing all the prisoners! When the prison guard realized that the doors were opened and the inmates were gone, he became depressed and tried to take his own life. However, Paul and Silas came out and stopped him. The guard asked them how he could be saved, and they told him that all he needed to do was to believe in Jesus. So the guard and his family were baptized by Paul.

PAUL SHIPWRECKED

(Acts 27:1-44)

Paul had been in and out of prison in Roman custody. He believed he was being treated unfairly by the Jews who were persecuting him, so he appealed his case to Caesar in Rome since he was a Roman citizen. So they set sail for Rome. As they sailed, a great storm formed on the sea for many days. However, Paul told them that they would not die. The ship ran across a reef on an island, and all 276 people aboard jumped overboard and swam to the island. Everybody was saved, just as Paul had said.

BUT THE

FRUIT OF THE SPIRIT

IS

LOVE, JOY,

PEACE, PATIENCE,

KINDNESS, GOODNESS,

FAITHFULNESS, GENTLENESS,

SELF-CONTROL;

AGAINST SUCH THINGS THERE IS
NO LAW.

Galatians 5:22-23

If you loved this book, please check out some of the other resources on our website!

The Old Testament: Made Amazingly Simple

More than 70% of The Bible

In many ways the Bible is like a puzzle with many pieces that individually are important but it's not until you put them all together that you see the bigger picture.

The Old Testament makes up 70% of the Bible puzzle.

The New Testament: Made Amazingly Simple

So, what would Jesus do?

It's a great question! In order to answer it, we must first answer the question, what did Jesus do?

The New Testament tell us about Christ's life on Earth from the people who where closest to him.

Heroes of The Bible: Made Amazingly Simple

Get to know the amazing Heroes that inspired The Bible!

The Bible is filled with complex stories. We've found it's easier to understand these stories when you get to know the people in them.

Heroes of The Bible fills you in on the most well-known heroes (and some not so heroic people) in The Bible.

Virtues of The Bible: Made Amazingly Simple

How does The Bible ACTUALLY tell us to live our lives?

Virtues are scattered all throughout the stories in The Bible and trying to grasp them on your own can seem overwhelming...

But understanding these Virtues is the most important lesson you'll gain from learning the Bible.

As a special 'thank you' to our customers, please use the coupon code below to save 15% on your next order:

COUPON CODE: BLESSED